For Mr P, Maxi-taxi, Chutney, Jo, Spammo & Gee

First published in Great Britain in 2018

Copyright: SerenArts Gallery

Written and Created by: Shreenie

All images by Shreenie ©

Book Design by: Mike Pugh

ISBN: 978-0-9932949-3-8

Published by:

SerenArts Publishing
Unit 3 Tithebarn Workshops
Pound Lane
Bradford on Avon
Wiltshire
BA15 1LF

Telephone: 01225 868644

Email: info@serenarts.co.uk

Website: www.serenarts.co.uk

Printed by:

Peter Leach
JFDi Print Services Ltd
10 Frome Road
Bradford on Avon
Wiltshire
BA15 1LB

Edited by:

Joceline Bury

A Serene View

of Bradford on Avon

Foreword

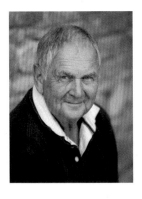

Some years ago I was privileged to be one of the exhibitors at the Bath and West Show. In those days the then West Wilts District Council sponsored a number of small businesses from the region in order to promote their work and products.

Adjoining my stand were a charming young couple, Serena and Mike Pugh. Mike had started up a small printing business while Serena was busy developing her considerable artistic talents in fine art, print making and photography. So began a long business association and friendship between the three of us.

Serena's fine art is both imaginative and skilled and, over the years, has been honed to a very high standard. In addition, she has developed this talent into the world of the printed image and, along with her photography, now produces the most innovative images for both private and commercial customers.

Serena showcases her work at the Seren Arts Gallery near the Tithe Barn in her home town of Bradford on Avon. Here one will find a constant selection of her latest work including original artwork, prints and framed photographs. Much of the work mirrors the world round her and includes many images of Bradford on Avon which are eagerly sought by her collectors and followers.

This book presents an opportunity to view some of Serena's finest work. The pictures are a joy to see and will provide readers with an opportunity to share some of the work of one of Wiltshire's exciting new artists.

Steve Hall
2018

Dedication

To my long suffering husband Mike ("No! It's not done like that!") for his ability to try and steer me in the right direction with traditional book design. Some of it actually worked. Thank you for untangling my ball of wool mind and laying my ideas down so beautifully. I know your working title for my book was 'Ramblings of a Deranged Mind' as you said this in your outside head voice instead of your inside head voice. You may have a point. Thank you for your love and support and making this whole process such fun... in the main!

Thanks go to our fabulous boys and their lovely ladies who give me no end of pleasure, and keep me uplifted day to day. This book is ultimately for them to keep and treasure, and maybe pass on to our long awaited grandchildren. (Family joke!)

Thank you to all my respective parents as well for their support over the years, especially financially! From good advice, hands on helping, fun evenings of unwinding or just leaving me be to get on with things, all of it has helped me get to this point in life and I am eternally grateful.

And lastly many thanks to Steve for his kind words. A true inspiration and wonderful man who has supported SerenArts over many years. There is always a brew ready for you, our friend.

Introduction

One of my earliest art related memories was of my exasperated mother corralling my younger brother and I up to the dining table, to paint a picture to enter in to the village fête that year. My brother lasted less than five minutes, but I painted a donkey giving children rides. I came first in my age group and won the princely sum of £1.50 (which I think is still £1.50 in this day and age). I bought three second hand books and a sponge cake from the same stall. Sharing the cake with my brother was every bit as exciting as what I imagine the Turner Prize would feel like. My life long love of art was born.

I was sent to boarding school (no doubt to hone my genius talent), and within a few years had won the English Essay Writing Shield which hadn't been given out in nearly a decade. I was all of thirteen years old and the next progression step would naturally be the Booker Prize, surely? To date, and more than thirty years on, I have not won a single thing since, unless you count the school record for fitting the most Cheddar Thins in my mouth. Nine, if you're interested.

These two singular instances in my youth planted deep, creative seeds that I have been fortunate enough to nurture, and encourage to fruition in my middle age. I have always felt there is a book of sorts in me and here it is.

For the past decade I have been running a small art gallery with my husband, in the idyllic medieval market town of Bradford on Avon. My artworks have encompassed many styles and genres over the years and I am always experimenting. My latest foray is in merging my photographs and art digitally, to create something different to offer. I am also presenting it in book form because I am running out of wall space and there is still too much 'artifartiness' inside me to contain.

Bradford on Avon is more than just a home or business for me. I have been the very worst, and best version of myself here. I have met with the most uplifting of highs in life here, and suffered through the hardest tragedies here too. I feel an affinity and deep affection for this town, like no other I have lived in. That doesn't stop me poking loving fun at it though. This may not be as traditional as most but no-one can fault my dedication to this sprawling jewel. Please enjoy my personal view.

Disclaimer: Some of this book may contain actual facts. I sincerely apologise for that.

Allergen advice: Vegetarian friendly, but may contain nuts.

I am a mischievous pain in the proverbial and have hidden my little flower logo with my initials as leaves on every single main picture. I think only three are actually easy to spot. You can thank me later. There is no point in emailing me for answers to where they are, as my brain forgets things 2.7 seconds after doing them. It is as much of a surprise to me when I find them again!

And on to the artwork...

I thought it would be a great idea to start the pictures part off with a dynamic, explosive image - but on reflection maybe I should have chosen something a little less black and white. This now looks like one of those adult colouring books popping up everywhere... albeit for adults after ten cups of espresso coffee.

'A Town Outline' - Bradford on Avon Townscape looking towards Trowbridge.

Five

'Abbey Mill'

Close up detail with a view through the archway to the Abbey Mill car park.

Thankfully this wall has been left untouched despite many renovations of the mill, and provides a beautiful focal point.

After much research I can honestly say I have no idea what this is called or who owns it - but it is the poshest piece of riverside decking I have seen in a long while. If it were mine, only nightfall would move me from here. I would even sit in a grade II listed deckchair so as not to upset the area's ambience.

i'd sit and watch
the world go by
everyday from
here . . .

Nine

Ten

Kids today...
Will never know the panic of trying to insert a 10 pence piece in to the slot as the beeps go...

A view of the phone box outside the Catholic Church, on the corner of Church Street and Market Street. I bet it has heard a few confessionals in its time!

I recently heard a small child in our gallery asking his father "what is that" about a phone box I had taken as a photo.

We all felt suddenly old...

Eleven

Twelve

Rolling on...

The river steals a march through the rocks,
the thin trickle seeping impervious,
collecting the rain as it drips and drops
in to the darkened world of Orpheus.

Deep it wanders through the limey ground,
pooling and spooling amongst the caves,
carving through fissures and cracks abound
searching for the lowest point it craves.

It broadens and meanders and opens out,
snaking its way through the medieval town.
Past the old mills and factories, looping about,
powering its flow under the bridge further down.

Undercurrents roll and tumble under the calm,
pushing on through past barn and workshops,
the fowl and swans bob without qualm,
on their cold, watery world that ne'er stops.

The expanse pummels the Packhorse with scant heed,
day in and out, squeezing underneath its stonework,
to banks lined with trees, where the kingfisher feeds,
on small minnows who hide in the murk.

Away it stretches for many a mile,
carrying activity along and its great seam,
to other river-sided towns of this fair Isle,
supporting life from the up, to downstream.

Rolling on, rolling away every day.

Fourteen

A big part of this town is its tourist friendly canal, so be warned fair reader, there will be many a picture of it dotted about in this book... I just cannot help myself. I have a major lack of willpower when it comes to certain locales here (and gourmet jelly beans but I digress). The canal is one of my favourite parts of Bradford on Avon. It is a working canal and hosts many businesses along its length - you can get a haircut, grab some cheese and order some wrought iron garden gates all before lunch time. Not bad hey? Cafés and pubs flank its sides for those in need of refreshment. Take a care though with the shandy as the water is at least 28 ducks worth high, and they are wholly useless at helping you back out of the murky water. A lack of opposable thumbs and no sense of duty, you see.

Some parts of the town date back to the 9th century, however the canal finally got going in 1794 when the first sod was cut, thus making it quite an old sod. John Rennie took some time off from making antacid tablets and re-routed old proposed sites to a more southerly, acceptable path. The man who said 'ye olde yes', Chuck Dundas, has part of the canal named after him. Rennie has to make do with his chalky pellet fame instead.

The town flourished with its new found transport system for over one hundred years until replaced with the more cost effective Great Western Railway line. Drawing trade away, it was left to fall into decline and eventually closed (just like my first blog). Luckily for us a massive restoration project brought the canal back to its former glory thanks to an army of volunteers including Edward VII and Sybil Fawlty. I kid you not. Okay, maybe a little, but Timothy West and his wife Prunella Scales lent their not inconsiderable weight to the restoration effort. Selfless volunteers still maintain the waterway. It is a beautiful stretch for the leisure boats and work barges alike, and a bustling hive of activity, as you will see a glimpse of over the page...

Seventeen

Eighteen

Serena Pugh

Nineteen

"Ahoy there matey!"
The shout goes out
as the barges slide gently by.
He turns one-eighty
waving airily about
to acknowledge the battle cry.

They mock salute
in a jovial way,
one brief captain to another.
The temporary commute
of the canal holiday
recognised by a fellow boat brother.

The Real Skipper !

He strolled amiably down the old towpath, weaving to one side as the tinny bell from a bicycle warned him of an imminent collision if he didn't step aside. He nimbly dodged the bike and the puddled pothole next to him, and watched the Lycra-clad rear end of a large, sweating woman flash by and thread through the milling Sunday tourists. He genuinely marvelled at the strength and give of the material as much as he did the willpower of the woman to ride a bike obviously designed to cut her in two. "Fair play" he mused to no one but himself, and carried on down the rocky pathway.

Up ahead, bearing scant regard to anything its owners had to say was a lolloping wolfhound slowly making its way towards him. Its tongue was hanging out to one side as it panted, and he watched as a silver line of saliva grew longer in the autumn sun, waving around as the animal plodded ever nearer. He tried side stepping and second guessing the animal, but to no avail. As the animal languidly bounced past it shook its head and he saw the great runnel of slimy dog spit arch and break off mid-air to land unceremoniously on his freshly ironed chinos. He disdainfully searched for a tissue in his pocket and came up trumps quickly wiping the offending gloop off his slacks. A thin wet line seeped into the material but he knew it would dry before he got to his destination, nonetheless he still kept a curled lip to show his displeasure as the owners passed him by. They both gave him a thousand yard stare over his shoulder as they hurried past refusing steadfastly to meet his gaze. He noticed however the woman of the couple colouring up, and he smiled inwardly at her show of embarrassment. To add a further flourish to her florid pallor he held his tissue out like it was steeped in pure poison, dangling from his outstretched fingertips. He bit the inside of his cheek to stop his grin from giving him away. The truth was that nothing could upset him on such a beautiful day, least of all a little canine mouthwash, and he beamed beatifically as they disappeared behind him. He could see a waste bin up ahead and he deposited his damp tissue, disturbing a few wasps making a meal from an ice lolly stick.

He turned off the towpath and wended his way through Barton Farm Country Park and the picnic blankets adorning the rolling grassy slopes, like a loosely strewn pack of discarded cards on the green baize of a gaming table. A happy babble of noise from families enjoying the warm autumnal day filled his ears, as people were making the most of the sunshine before the cold damp days started creeping in. He followed the tarmac walkway snaking past the pale medieval buildings and rounded the corner to the Tithebarn Workshops. "At last a cuppa" he thought to himself, as he espied an A board indicating a tearoom and garden.

He looked around and found the little café sandwiched between two art galleries. He sat down at one of the painted wooden tables looking towards the other units. He picked up the menu more out of curiosity than hunger and toyed with the idea of a scone or two. The sound of flip-flops traipsing toward him made him lift his head and he ordered a cup of tea from the owner who stopped long enough from telling his wife the finer points of rugby, to ask for his order. He smiled when their conversation restarted mid-sentence as only couples appear to do.

He set the menu down tidily, as he had found it, and gradually let his eyes roam over the surroundings taking in the renovated old cow sheds. The two long, stone barns ran at right angles to each other and made from the creamy coloured Bath stone that the area was noted for. Internal walls sectioned the units off and each window fronted display was a colourful array of the contents of the shop. His eyes rested on the last workshop where a myriad of antique chairs were set out, and he sat bemused watching a Jack Russell trampolining at the window of its owners car. He chuckled as a teenager with slick, coiffed hair stopped and leant towards the glass to check his primped reflection, only to leap back in shock, barely keeping his feet, and seriously denting his street credibility, as the dog snapped and ferociously yapped at him for daring to invade its personal space.

His pot of tea arrived quickly and with brewing instructions, and he set about sorting himself for 'a decent cuppa'. A burst of hilarity came from the eclectic gallery next door and an electric blue origami bird shot out of the open door forcefully, to drop like a stone just past the doorstep. He heard giggling voices inside agreeing that 'we should really leave origami to the experts and get on with some work' and he wondered what tea they were drinking, and more importantly, could he get some too.

Four ladies standing by the corner of the buildings laughed raucously at a shared joke, and he smiled with them infectiously as they disbanded and disappeared back into their respective shops. He leaned back against the stonework soaking up the warmth of the sun as he sipped his cuppa. Leaves intermittently dropped off the cherry trees before him, as the Autumn air swirled in short bursts across the garden. Through the thinning branches he could make out blue tits and robins vying for dinner rights as they argued lyrically over the bird feeders, ignoring the tourists and locals as they meandered by. He thought to himself 'what a perfect place to work'....

and he is not wrong dear reader! It is so nice down here it's a mild embarrassment to actually call it work. I still think 'let's go play!' as we set off each day to earn a crust. I am a very lucky lady (okay! Who coughed just then?) to enjoy the space down here. This side of the Tithe Barn area is like a well kept secret at times, as most people walk past to go straight to the very impressive 14th century barn. Many a time we hear locals saying 'I never knew this place existed!', like we are situated on Platform 9 ¾ waiting for Harry Potter. This is my not needed excuse for a lengthy, drawn out advertisement.

Twenty Four

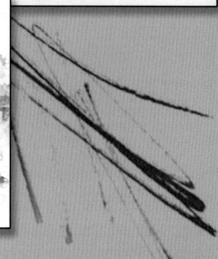

Twenty Six

This was taken on Christmas Eve 2013, this is the downside of running a gallery on the banks of a river. It is pretty in its own way, however not so nice mopping up afterwards!

Good for the swans but not great for business!

Twenty Eight

Twenty Nine

The TitheBarn

Thirty One

Thirty Two

Once upon a time a well-minted, superfluity of nuns from Shaftesbury were given this Manor land by Æthelred the Unready, to inter his murdered, half-brother's bones, Edward the Martyr.

Lordy. Imagine being given that name as a child... you know it's not going to end well.

Who sent him off to his martyrdom you may ask. Why, the evil stepmother Ælfryth (pronounced 'elf risk'!) and her stabby supporters of course. It sounds like a medieval episode of 'Jerymye Kylle the Muckraker': When ye olde step-mums go bad.'

To absolve any guilt he may have felt Æthelred gave Bradford Manor land over to the nuns so they would look after the nearly kingly remains in the appropriate manner. Many moons later they built a big barn amongst other things.

This is how we came to have our 14th century Tithe Barn, one of the largest and most beautiful grade I listed buildings of its type in the country, all thanks to the 'supposed, skeleton enshrining, substantially swollen money sacked, as yet unsuppressed, shed erecting Shaftesbury sisters'.

To this date there has been no mention in history that the bones were ever laid to rest here.

Poor Edward the Lost in Transit...

Thirty Four

Serena Pugh

Serena Pugh

Thirty Five

Thirty Six

My husband is rolling his eyes. I am being far too jocular. I think some respect is due for the big ol' barn. It really is a stunning building. It is over 50 metres long, and has stood the test of time since the 14th century. It sits proudly in what was old farmland, nestled amongst the other smaller buildings. Our workshops on the land are in fact the old skillins (that's cow byres to you and me!), that have been renovated.

Inside the Tithe Barn the original timber cruck roof is the jewel, I think, of the whole area. It is a magnificent piece of architecture and skill. Looking down you can still see evidence of grain threshing on the stone floor. The barn is host to many a swallow during the summer months and a bat or two. I occasionally see a heron resting solitary on the roof catching the sun, so the barn is quite a draw for tourists and nature alike.

These few pages are various views of the Barton Farm area

Tithe Barn
that-a-way

The Workshops this-a-way

Forty

Serena Pu

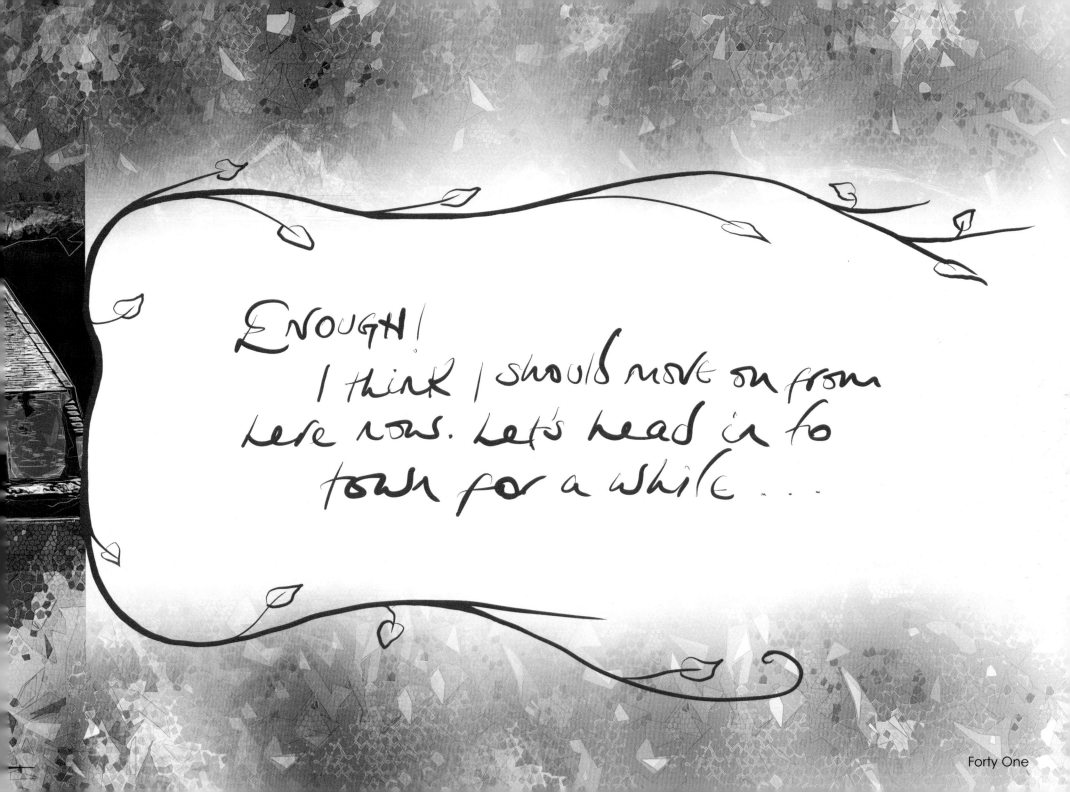

ENOUGH!
I think I should move on from
here now. Let's head in to
town for a while . . .

The Town Bridge

Forty Three

Forty Four

Forty Five

Forty Six

"Under the fish & over the water"

A view of the Town Bridge complete with Lock Up.
The weather vane is a glistening gudgeon atop the old Chapel/Lock Up, so anyone inside the small building could be said to be "under the fish and over the water".

The bridge over the river in the town centre is the most iconic landmark here. Originally it was built for packhorses and footfall to traverse the broad ford space (yes! That's where Bradford on Avon gets its name), but over the years it has been widened to allow for the vigorous change in transport.

The original side is a veritable feast of pointy Norman architecture and houses a small stone building which was used as a chapel, and then at the other end of the spectrum, the town's lock up for the wayward.

The latter side of the bridge is as plain as a Rich Tea biscuit in a world of Viennese Whirls. It reminds me of when our children first helped decorate the Christmas tree. There would be half a hundred weight of sparkly tinsel and glittered baubles on the front - and not a solitary bead on the back. I would wait discreetly until they had gone to bed, before tugging the festive finery like a glistening fishing net Midas would have been proud of, back over the bare bits.

The cat would then discreetly wait for us to go to bed...

The Rich Tea side of the bridge →

Serena Pugh

Forty Nine

Thomas in the Lock up

I have always wondered what it would be like to spend a night here in the lock up...

The inky black behind his eyes began to give way to a swirling, misty red but they still refused to open. As each second ticked by his other senses unfortunately woke up to their surroundings, and he realised he was freezing cold. Where was he? A full body tremble assaulted him for a minute until he managed to gain some control over himself. He let his teeth chatter on uncontrollably, the staccato sound strangely comforting in his head. At the mention of his head he felt a blinding stab of pain wake up inside his skull. He tried lifting his hands to hold himself together but they refused to budge from his sides, instead just showing a little flutter from his fingers. His headache thumped and pulsed viciously, throbbing so badly behind his eyes he feared they would be pushed out of their sockets. He groaned and his stomach lurched dangerously. The roaring in his ears seemed so loud he felt it had leaked out and was swirling through the air around his prone form. His brow wrinkled in concern. What in God's name was that noise? He slowly came round a little more and heard the noise for what it was. Water. Lots of it. Rushing and thundering underneath him.

"How is that possible?" he thought to himself. His fingers felt in trepidation around his sides. Stone. Cold wet stone. Dawn's light was shining weakly through several square, window like holes, and his eyes started to make out his surroundings. He lifted his head up off the floor and the movement caused his precarious stomach contents to hurl themselves violently up through his body, and explode from his mouth in a bitter, acidic outburst. Two thoughts hit him simultaneously as he stared at the green bilious offering he had graced the floor with. Never drink seven mugs of honeyed mead on an empty stomach, and never, ever drink so much mead you are thrown in the town's lock up.

He moaned loudly to no-one but himself, and dragged himself over to the hole in the corner of the cell. He watched the murky river race past below and debated whether to drop his breeches to relieve his insides of their toxic contents, but luckily the water motion decided for him, and he expelled another load orally through the stinking cess hole. He managed a wry smile as there was several seconds of waiting, before the satisfying splashes of liquid on liquid floated back up to his ears. He imagined the pike and gudgeon being less than happy with his choice of fish food.

His head started swimming and he pulled himself into a sitting position against the furthest wall from the privy, panting and sweating with the effort. His world span and he felt truly sorry for himself. He realised unhappily he was not going to die of mead poisoning but he was beginning to feel it might be a far nicer alternative to waiting the poison out. He buried his head in his hands feeling a little relief as the heel of his palms pressed into his aching eyeballs.

Images began to flood his memory in fragments at first, but then great chunks of sudden realisation bombarded him of his antics the night before. He cringed inwardly at his high jinks. Ye Gods, he was easily led! But he knew that to be a lie, he knew exactly what he was doing most of the time, and actively enrolled any drinking companion he could find to join him, however unsuitable and regardless of age and gender. He smirked faintly to himself as he recalled an infamous drinking night at the Bear with Olde Widow Forde. He got her so out of her cups on pumpkin wine, they renamed an area of the bar after her. She had never forgiven him and never set foot in the place again, but many of the patrons still recanted the story of how 'soggy bottom corner' had been so named after a soused old woman had copiously wet her pantaloons, being too drunk to make it outside.

Suddenly he felt what little colour he might have had in his face drain downwards, leaving a damp sheen of sweat, like a dewy death mask. The very air around him shimmered and bent and he felt a constriction in his throat. He tried to call out as shapes swirled in ghostly colours around him, but his voice stuck inside his throat. He watched, his eyes bulging as if to take more of the surroundings in, transfixed as the air grew more solid. Eventually the scene resolved,

and he could make out a pious man kneeling in the cell with him. He was so shocked he couldn't utter a foul oath, and tried to scurry back away from the apparition. He was already up against the wall so his legs just pedalled furiously back and forth, his heels scraping along the cold stones.

He noticed his frenetic movements made not the slightest difference to the kowtowed figure as if they could not see him, and he slowly pulled his heart back in to his body and became still. His overloaded brain tried to make sense of the scene amid his terror and he realised the man was praying, the ghostly visitor's fingertips pressed lightly together in supplication, his lips mouthing silent words. Thomas decided with alacrity he should do the same and he garbled a plea to any deity that may have been listening to him.

His cries bounced around the confined space as he shouted out "Merciful God! Save my poor soul!". He gibbered, spit dripping down his chin, wailing out again "Can you hear me Lord?".

His heart nearly stopped as he heard a booming knock on the wooden door and a loud, gruff voice calling his name. "Thomas?"
"Lord is that you?" he sobbed.
"No you drunken old sot" the voice came back. "Gads man, you were in your cups last night. It's Jon. You better set your breeches straight. It's a trip to the magistrates for you. I'm opening up".

Thomas stood and edged towards the wooden door, his back pressed so hard against the wall he could feel every rough lump dig into him. The shimmering vision undulated and grew less bright as the door opened. Thomas lunged wild eyed out on to the day-lit bridge pathway.

A strong hand clamped over his shoulder halting his flight and the lawman asked if his clam diggers were on fire.
"Not so fast" he chided. "You got an 'ansome fine coming

Thomas. Lord Powlett is none too pleased with you lettin' his kine out for sure".

Thomas looked back at the lock up furtively and thought any amount of punishment would be preferable to staying where he was. He emphatically swore an oath he would never let a single drop of anything fermented pass his lips again - Mrs Forde would just have to find herself another pard to get snockered with!

"Are you alright Thomas?" the lawman asked "You look like you seen a ghost, cully. 'Course it could just be the ale all sour in your belly".

Thomas walked as fast as he could. If only you knew he thought as the distance lengthened, but carefully kept quiet about his mirage. It was going to be a long time before the mockery of his previous night's shenanigans were going to die down. Best not to add more fuel he thought.

"I'm good Jon, lets get this sorted "eh?" Thomas said over his shoulder a little too eagerly. As he strode he gradually warmed up to the point he felt his thirst sneak up on him, his tongue dryly sticking in his mouth. "Ah but for a cup of mead" he mused as his feet turned towards the nearest pub.

Fifty Three

Fifty Four

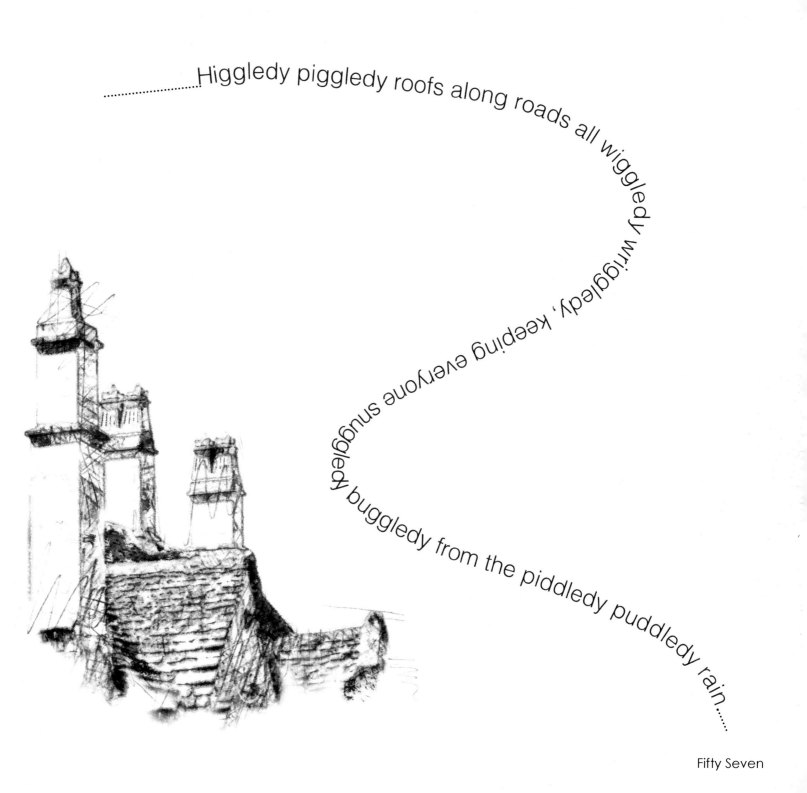

Higgledy piggledy roofs along roads all wiggledy wriggledy, keeping everyone snug buggledy from the piddledy puddledy rain ......

Although modern in design these new builds have echoes
of the triangular roofs of the old factories in town. Sort of.

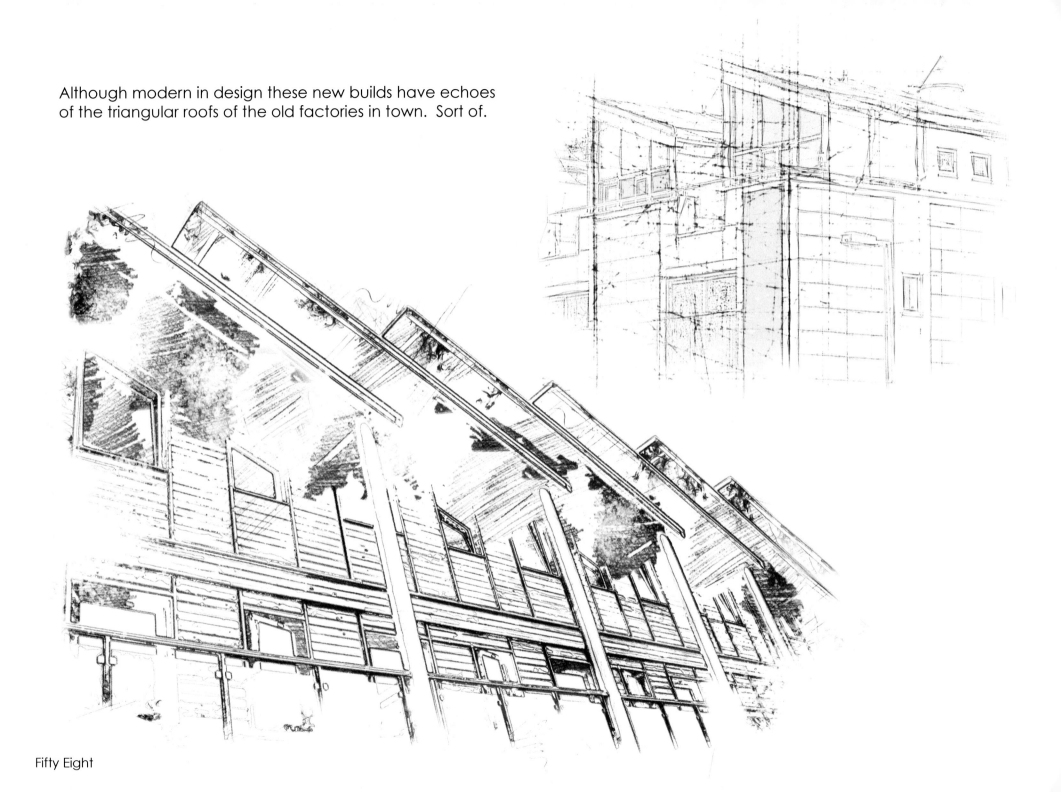

Fifty Nine

↑ I love this Roof

Views of the Wesleyan Methodist Chapel, the Town and the Roundhouse.

On to some golden oldies...

Sixty One

Sixty Two

Sixty Three

'Silver Street'

It is always good to include a few
examples of earlier works - the
comparisons show progression.

'Westbury Gardens Bus Stop and War Memorial'

Sixty Seven

If stone could talk...

The Bath stone glows warm in the waning sunlight,
enduring endless elements with all its might,
silently absorbing each spoken thought we say,
glistening and listening innocuously day by day.
It soaks up condensation from our smatters of chatter,
paying no heed to diverse accents and patois,
ignoring our discourses amid each concourse,
solidly deaf to whispered longings or insults coarse.
Impassively it stands, towering all around us,
held together by cement, flying buttress and truss,
as we orate the minutiae of our lives within its reach -
our secrets imparted forever kept safe from breach.
May the Bath stone hold its quiet counsel we can but pray,
for if stone could talk... what would it say?

*Before all the English academia turn harrumphy and blustery, this is just a
little pseudo-sonnet. I could have gone full on Petrarchan but the rhyming
schematics always make me want to sing "tonight the super trouper beams
are gonna find me" and wear lots of light blue eye liner...*

Coppice Hill

Sixty Nine

Every now and then as an artist you are asked to contribute to projects and collaborations, and I was honoured recently to be involved in the promotional side of an historical project in town. The old mills here that were once engaged in producing textiles, gradually gave way to more modern business, mainly the manufacture of rubber goods.

To this end an iconic, specialised, calender machine was built in 1849, called The Iron Duke, and was the first of its kind in Europe. It served the town well for a century, but in 1972 Kingston Mill was demolished and the Iron Duke dismantled.

Fast forward 45 years and the town has seen a vast change in its construct. The old mills are now luxury apartments, restaurants or independent retail shops, and the earlier, textile-rich heritage of the town has given way naturally, to the more modern life. To keep our history alive, a joint effort by the Preservation Trust, the Museum and BOA can here, saw the Iron Duke brought back to Bradford on Avon, and reassembled to form a unique landmark. Other projects and further reading on this subject can be found on the Avon Works website.

For my small part, here are the pieces I was commissioned to do, relating to the town's industrial backdrop, with a modern twist. These six images depict aspects of life at the Avon over the years.

I threaded a list of the main sponsors through the Iron Duke rollers as a nod to all their combined hard work and to show how the calender machine worked. To think back in its heyday this machine had scant regard for health and safety. I bet you would remember your lesson if it nibbled at your fingers.

The beer mug with the old factory in it was to highlight the social side of life through the town. In the era before food-led public houses, there were not many watering holes which did not have a customer who had worked at the Avon at some point, or knew someone. I'm not suggesting the workers were alcoholics before anyone gets a tad sniffy at me, but rather, the town is small and the workforce always well numbered in its day.

The tennis ball work is a straightforward representation of one of the rubber products manufactured. I liked the idea that at one point in its history Avon Rubber's world revolved around the humble tennis ball. The buildings on top are the factories with the two chimneys showing - quite the iconic landmarks at one point.

To the right is a piece documenting the demise of the old buildings. I wanted to show that just about everything has a shelf life. Through my grungy art contribution I believe you can still see some of the majesty these huge buildings held on the landscape, no matter how decrepit they eventually became.

Overleaf shows firstly imagery of the mainly female workforce that kept the factories producing goods through the two world wars. The wreath motif is based on the plaque erected in memoriam to the fallen who never made it back to town.

Seventy Three

Seventy Four

And secondly here, the Gatehouse where each worker had to clock in and out of daily. I wonder how many times the machine punched the work slips? More than my fingers and toes can count, that's for sure. If any ex-employee reading this was never too happy about clocking on first thing Monday morning, don't worry - I kind of exploded it end of era style. You can thank me later.

What's next?

Seventy Six

Other sentinels standing proud in the Bradford skyline are our imposing churches. We can boast a ninth century Saxon church in good repair which draws tourists to the town, along with the Tithe Barn. It is actually quite a lovely little, no nonsense building as far as churches go in my opinion. I am probably not the best person to write about them as I find most are dark, cold and huge, with hymn books that smell of gerbils, but I can appreciate the architecture involved. Who doesn't like a few grandiose spires dotting the horizon?

These artworks in order show Christ Church, Holy Trinity, The Chapel of St Mary Tory and the Saxon Church. There are several other more modern churches tucked away offering many choices for a variety of religious denominations, so faith is well supported here.

I cannot tell you what most look like on the inside being the irreligious heathen I am. I did nearly have a religious experience though climbing the Tory hill steps to get to St Mary's. Why is there no oxygen medical station at the top? And I do sing Christmas carols loudly when I can, (usually in June), but I am not sure this qualifies me as any sort of tour guide. Ho hum. Maybe someone else can write a book on church interiors here. I will throw in a snappy title for free - "Inside Religion". What do you reckon? Okay I will shush now.

Wait! Just one more quick aside. There are twice as many churches as there are public conveniences in town. There are only three I can think of for about nine thousand people. We had better pray we don't need the loo while out and about!

It is said the town's folk of Bradders,
Have infeasibly minuscule bladders.
So please have a care,
As you walk everywhere,
To steer clear of the Bath stone shadders!

Seventy Eight

Seventy Nine

Eighty One

The Swan

The next few pages are a nod to some of the public houses in the town centre. There are quite a few watering holes dotted around the town in many a nook and cranny, but many have closed over the last decade or so, coincidentally, that runs parallel to my much needed sobriety! I do hope my taking the pledge all these years has nothing to do with the decline of the wet sales through town.

The pubs that are left open now, have incorporated busy food sides to stay afloat, so the old spit and sawdust 'boozers' are almost all gone. There are no such culinary delicacies as a two year old pickled egg in a packet of crisps. It is more likely to be a smoked kedgeree quail scotch egg, nestled artfully atop a presentation of hand made, stained glass, chervil crisps, with truffle oil and Himalayan pink rock salt. I'm hungry now.

There is no rhyme or reason to picking the buildings I have, other than two I worked for in another lifetime, (it was that long ago), and their proximity when carrying my camera.

© Thanks Jake!

One of my past reincarnations was as a chambermaid here in my early twenties. I had way too much energy back then and fit as a fiddler's elbow, but without the common sense to balance it. I was ebullient beyond annoying and up for anything. Looking back, my employers must have shaken their heads many a time at some of my antics. The trick to staying employed for me was to make myself available for bar work and waitressing too, therefore becoming as indispensable as possible.

I nearly got sacked one day for bringing the Swan's reputation into disrepute. I had picked up the list of rooms to clean and decided to make a start on room eight. It was to be a total change over ready for next guests. No problem. The room was vacant already as the occupant had finished breakfast and staff had seen them loading their luggage into their car.

Out of politeness I called out in warning that I was entering and on hearing nothing, bounced in like I owned the place. Room eight has the best view up the high street and the picture below shows how beautiful the actual window setting is. Before I started stripping the bed down I took a quick look out of the window and saw my friend (and fellow chambermaid) looking downcast, as she was making a phone call across the way. I waved and pulled a funny face and couldn't make her raise a smile. And then I had a wonderful idea!

I knew how to make her laugh. So right there in the middle of the window I undid my blouse and pulled my 'girls' out! I jiggled my jubblies for all I was worth and that is precisely when the bathroom door opened, and a very respectable looking, middle aged man stepped out in to the room. He just stood there completely agog. Wordless.

Dear reader, I fled past him out of the room faster than Usain Bolt.

I rearranged myself and knew I had to go down and apologise for my behaviour to the owner. So off I traipsed. I was receiving a verbal warning about the hotel's reputation (deservedly), when to my horror the man came down to reception to hand his key in. I was beetroot colour from embarrassment, but when he was asked if he had enjoyed his stay, the man answered without a moments hesitation.

"Oh yes. Especially the hot and cold running chambermaid! I do hope she's not getting in trouble over me - I must use this place again!"

... Luckily even my boss laughed.

ALE, PIE & CIDER HOUSE

← The Bear

The Castle →

I am glad these topiary balls are high up and out of my reach. They remind me of those executive toys on every desk in the nineties with the clanking, suspended steel balls.... and I just want to set them swinging.

Mela
Dole
Sale

THE CASTLE INN

FREEH'USE THE CASTLE INN FREEH'USE

Eighty Five

'Timbrell's Yard'

Eighty Six

'What a dandy lion you are'

Eighty Seven

This is the Bunch of Grapes in its new skin. Back in the day it has had many a fine darts team - sporty pubs are becoming much harder to find these days.

Moving along now towards the newer cafés and bistros that have rejuvenated the old Avon Mill area. The new part of town is filling rapidly and has a vibrant feel.

This is the Grounded Cafe - they took my collaborative work, so I am returning the favour and giving them a shout out in my book!

Eighty Nine

THE
WEAVING
SHED

Ninety

'The Weaving Shed'

Creative townsfolk addressing the
lack of parking in Bradford.

'Sebastien's Bistro'

Ninety Two

This is what the old Avon Mill site looked like and this is what it has become...

'Lamb's Yard'

Ninety Five

Ninety Six

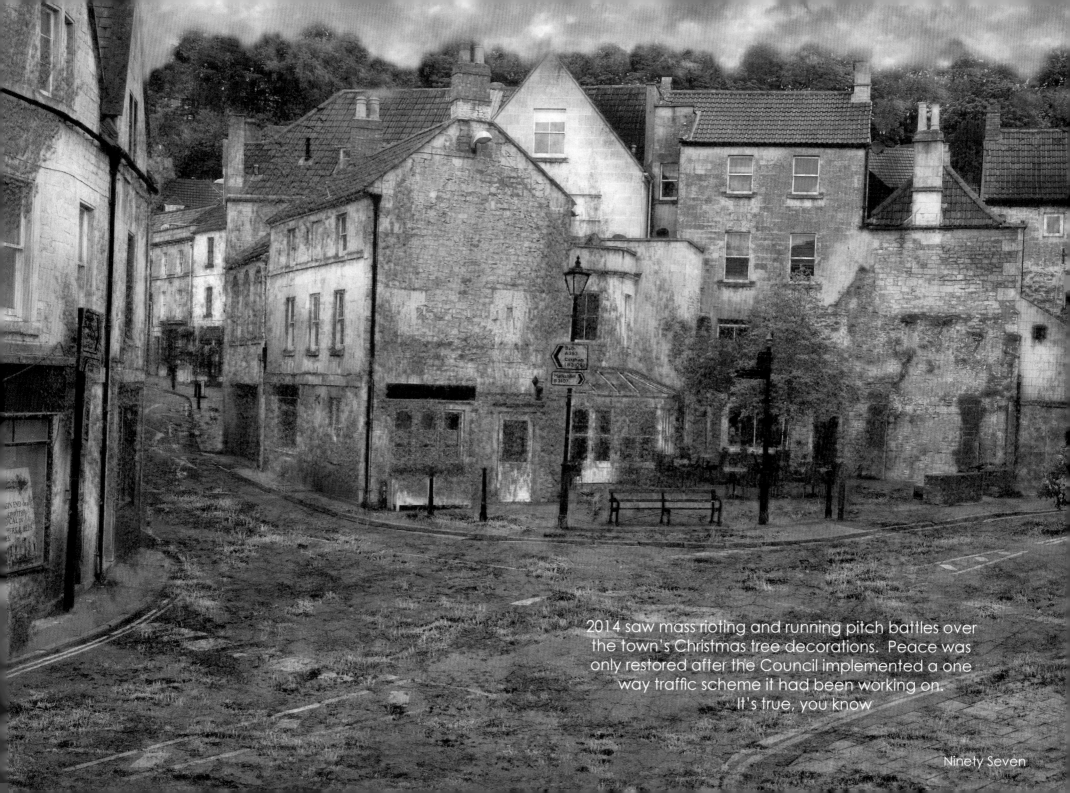

2014 saw mass rioting and running pitch battles over the town's Christmas tree decorations. Peace was only restored after the Council implemented a one way traffic scheme it had been working on.
It's true, you know

Ninety Seven

It struck me that I have managed to keep this book largely free of traffic and population in lieu of artistic integrity. It's a busy town in reality, so this took some doing.

As you can see from this picture the traffic in town can be quite concentrated through the centre, and the old, narrow roads struggle to cope with the modern demand. Every couple of years there are discussions to incorporate a one-way system, but as of yet there is no change to volume passing through.

We are well served however, by good bus routes and a picturesque train station. Old steam trains pass through regularly and generate a buzz for train spotters and picture takers alike.

The valley the town sits in has a view down through it, looking over the four main modes of transport through the years. Road, rail, canal and river have all played their part in keeping Bradford on Avon moving.

My husband is now muttering that its a short trip between Greenland Mill and Avoncliff where the two weirs bookend the town. I am contesting that the river was used to transport textiles before the weirs arrived... I win because its still a mode of transport no matter how short the trip!

N° 4492

Ninety Nine

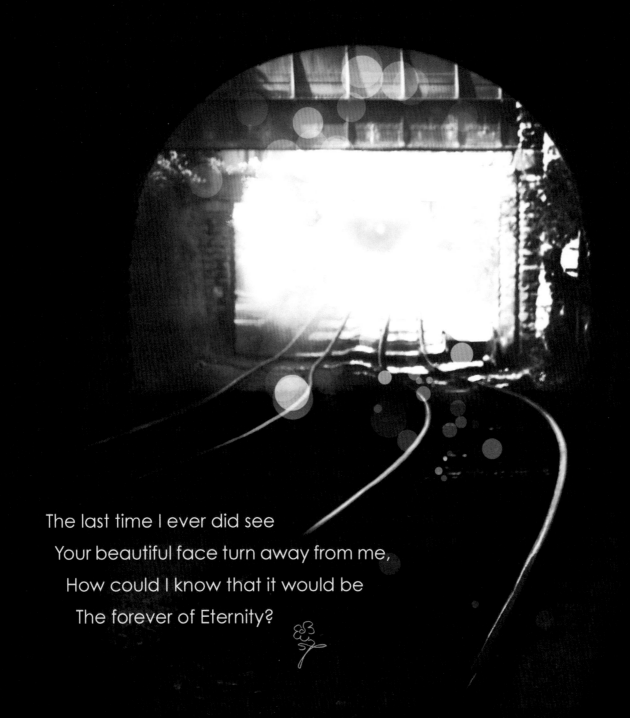

The last time I ever did see
Your beautiful face turn away from me,
How could I know that it would be
The forever of Eternity?

I sit on the edge of my ruined heart, pale lower legs idly grazing against the slick, sloping wall, letting my seven league feet dangle over the inky, black nothingness below.

I press my palms in to the spongy muscle I am sat on, readying myself for a determined push, using my fingernails to grip in to the squishy surface. A wry smile plays over my wordless lips as no feeling registers through my grief-laden system. Not even a twitch or a misfiring synapse to hold me back from sliding purposefully down the cold and mottled incline, to the welcoming abyss beckoning.

For I know you are there.

I feel you in the corner of my heart that was forever torn brutally from it's fleshy mooring, and left to float detached inside my body, the day you were wrenched away in death.

And as sure as you are there, and though searching may take immeasurable aeons between the breaths of the universe....

I know I will find you again, my son.

I know.

Meet the lovely Millie, a life-sized bronze statue sculpted by Dr J Willats, to mark the turn of the second millennium. She stands proudly in the centre of town and links the past, present and future of Bradford on Avon.

Name: Millie 2000 S, GSOH, NS (although I don't look a day older than my unveiling).

Job Title: Town protectress, and 19th c. fashionista.

Hobbies: Snatching birds clean out of the air, and spearing jelly bears on long sticks.

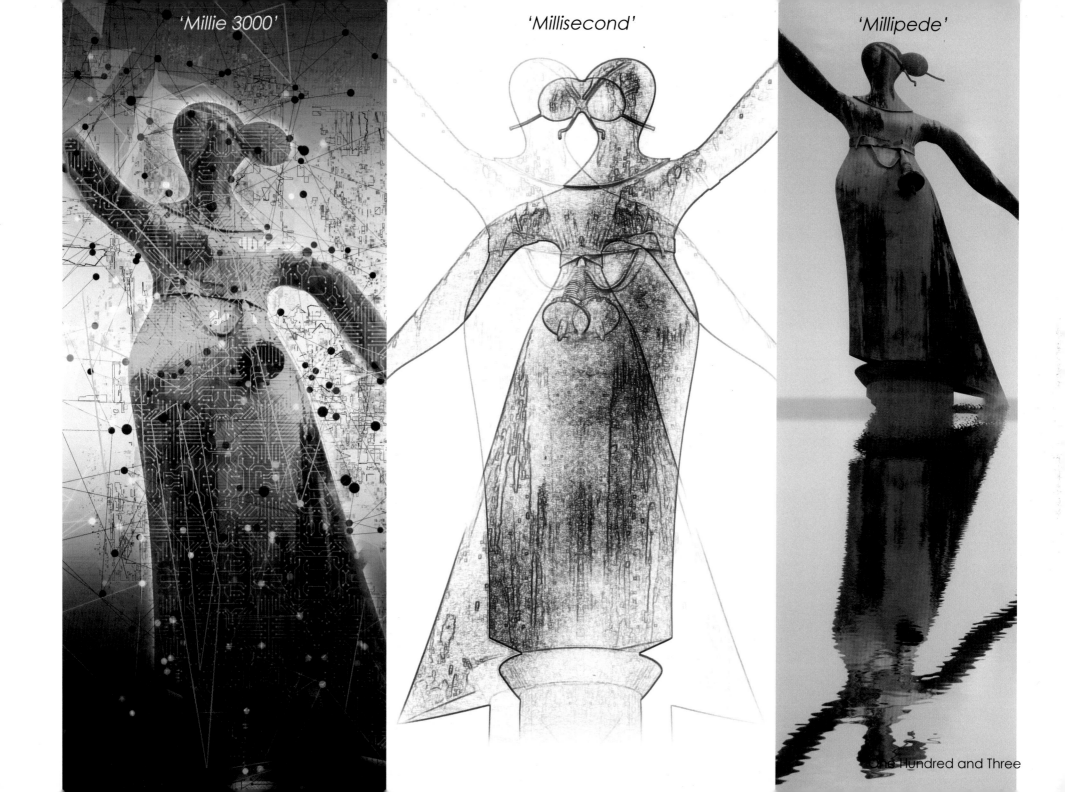

'Millie 3000'

'Millisecond'

'Millipede'

The Shambles

POST OFFICE

NEWS
Tudor
CARDS

One Hundred and Five

'Abbey House'

One Hundred and Six

'Preservation Trust HQ'

One Hundred and Seven

The library car park doubles up as the market every Thursday morning, a chance for producers to bring their wares to the town and an excellent shopping experience for locals.

'The Wharf'

One Hundred and Ten

My husband and I used to go fair weather kayaking on the river. I thought that this weir was as far as anyone could go upstream, but he had other ideas. He likes a challenge. Long story short, he made me climb up here with my kayak. I am still not sure if I've ever forgiven him. When you do manage to battle the sheer volume of icy, cold water cascading over your head, you are met by a blanket of slippery, treacherous, weed covered concrete at the top, hell bent on upending you. Which it did. Many times. I have the balance of blancmange on a bed of Vaseline at the best of times. I eventually ended up traversing the top on my behind, getting covered in swamp muck as I went. To add insult to injury from across the water a man could be heard braying with laughter at me, so my husband joined in. Charming!

'Tory'

'Middle Rank'

'Barton Orchard'

I think this is a good note to end the book on. These faces flanked the old cash machine in Church Street. I feel I have gone through all the emotions writing this book, between tragedy and comedy and everything in between. I hope you have been entertained by this personal peek into Bradford on Avon. I know I thoroughly enjoyed creating the book.

My face when I hide my sweets successfully from the kids...

My face when the kids have found my secret stash of sweets.

And finally

I tried to include as much as possible of Bradford on Avon but it is a big town and I only have size four feet. If I missed you out there is always another book in me. Until then...

adieu

I think this is a good note to end the book on. These faces flanked the old cash machine in Church Street. I feel I have gone through all the emotions writing this book, between tragedy and comedy and everything in between. I hope you have been entertained by this personal peek into Bradford on Avon. I know I thoroughly enjoyed creating the book.

My face when I hide my sweets successfully from the kids...

My face when the kids have found my secret stash of sweets.

And finally

I tried to include as much as possible of Bradford on Avon but it is a big town and I only have size four feet. If I missed you out there is always another book in me. Until then...

adieu